This book belongs to ...

....

Tips for Talking and Reading Together

Stories are an enjoyable and reassuring way of introducing children to new experiences.

Before you read the story:

- Talk about the title and the picture on the cover. Ask your child what they think the story might be about.
- Talk about what a doctor does. Has your child ever been to the doctor with you?

Read the story with your child. After you have read the story:

- Discuss the Talk About ideas on page 27.
- Talk about the things you find at the doctor on pages 28 – 29 and then find them in the pictures of the story.
- Do the fun activity on page 30.

Have fun!

Find the tiger cubs hidden in every picture.

For more hints and tips on helping your child become a successful and enthusiastic reader look at our website www.oxfordowl.co.uk.

Going to the Doctor

Written by Roderick Hunt
and Annemarie Young
Illustrated by Alex Brychta

OXFORD
UNIVERSITY PRESS

The children were excited. Miss Green was telling
them about a visit to the zoo. They were going at the end
of the week.

4

She showed them a picture of two tigers. "The zoo saved these tigers from the hunters," said Miss Green. "Let's find out about tigers."

Sam and Anna went to look at the tiger books
on the table.

"Come on Kipper," said Sam. "Help us find a good one."

But Kipper didn't feel well. He sneezed. He felt hot and he had a runny nose. His throat was sore and his head ached.

Anna went to Miss Green. "Kipper is crying," she said.
"He doesn't feel well," said Sam.

Miss Green felt Kipper's head. "You do feel hot, Kipper. I think you should go home. I'm going to call your mummy."

Mum came to take Kipper home. Kipper was upset. He didn't want to be ill. He wanted to see the tigers at the zoo.

"I think we should go and see my friend Aza. She's a nurse at the Health Centre," said Mum. "We'll go on the way home."

Aza looked at Kipper's throat and then took his temperature.

"My ear hurts a bit, too," said Kipper.

"Keep him at home," said Aza. "Give him lots to drink. Come back if his earache gets worse."

Mum let Kipper lie on the sofa. She gave him a book about tigers.

"I want to see the tigers at the zoo," said Kipper.

14

That night, Kipper woke up. "My ear really hurts," he said, "and there's stuff coming out of it."

Dad gave Kipper some medicine.

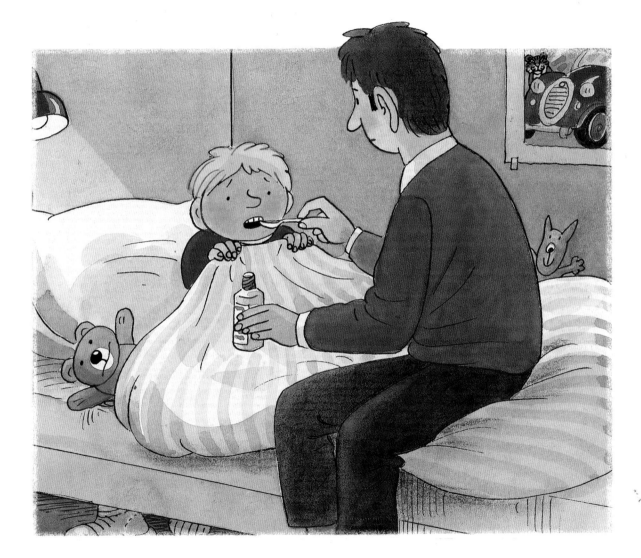

The next day, Kipper felt worse.

"We'd better go and see the doctor," said Dad.

"The nurse told us to go back if your ear got worse."

Kipper and Dad waited for the doctor to call them.

"You'll like Dr Spooner," said Dad. "She's really kind."

Dr Spooner listened to Kipper's chest and took his temperature. Then she looked in his ears.

"Poor Kipper," said Dr Spooner. "You've got an ear infection. I'll give you some ear drops and some medicine to take."

"I want to see the tigers with my class tomorrow," said Kipper.

"I'm sorry," said Dr Spooner. "You have to wait until your ear is better."

By Sunday, Kipper felt a lot better. His ear had stopped aching, but he was sad that he had missed the trip to see the tigers.

Sam came to see Kipper with Wilf and Wilma.
Sam was their cousin.

"I hurt my arm," said Sam, "so I didn't see the
tigers, either."

Just then, Mum came in. "We've got a surprise for you," she said.

Mum and Dad took them all to the zoo!

"The tigers are fantastic," said Kipper.

"They're so big," said Sam.

"What's that tiger doing?" asked Kipper.

"The tiger sneezed!" laughed Sam. "I think it has a cold."

"I hope it doesn't have an earache too!" said Kipper.

Talk about the story

Why was Kipper upset at school?

What did Dr Spooner tell Kipper?

Why did Mum and Dad take the children to the zoo?

What makes you feel better when you are ill?

What do you find at the doctor?

Talk about the things you see on this page. Can you think of anything else you might find at the doctor?
The doctor uses these things to …

measure your height

measure your weight

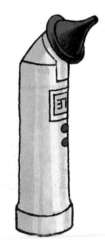

take your temperature

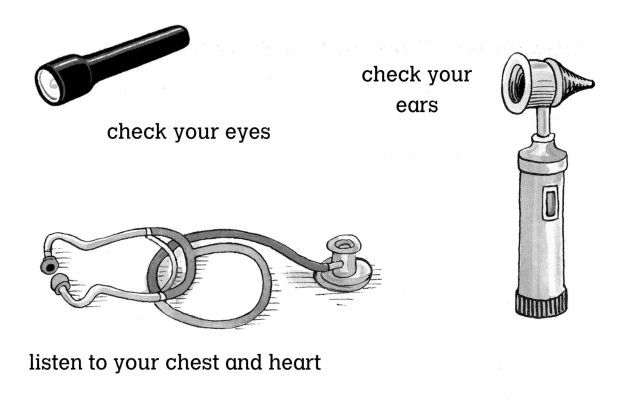

check your eyes

check your
ears

listen to your chest and heart

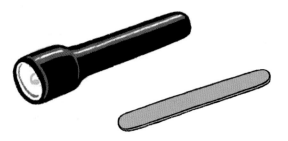

look inside
your mouth

Now look back at the story and find these things in
the pictures.

Spot the difference

Find the 5 differences in the two tiger cubs.

FIRST EXPERIENCES WITH Biff, Chip & Kipper

Have you read them all yet?

Kipper's First Pet

Learning to Swim

Going to the Dentist

Going to the Doctor

Going to the Hairdresser

Fun at the Farm

Going on a Plane

Starting School

FIRST EXPERIENCES Flashcards
55 cards

Also available:
- Kipper Gets Nits!
- At the Hospital
- At the Optician
- Bottles, Cans, Plastic Bags
- On a Train
- At the Vet
- At the Match
- At the Dance Class

Read with Biff, Chip and Kipper
The UK's best-selling home reading series

Phonics   **First Stories**

	Phonics	First Stories
Level 1 Getting ready to read	Kipper's Alphabet I Spy; Chip's Letter Sounds; Biff's Wonder Words; Floppy's Fun Phonics	Get On; Floppy Did This!; Up You Go; Six in a Bed
Level 2 Starting to read	I am Kipper; Cat in a Bag; The Red Hen; The Fizz-Buzz	Funny Fish; Silly Races!; The Snowman; Dad's Birthday
Level 3 Becoming a reader	Such a Fuss; Shops; The Sing Song; The Backpack	Poor Old Rabbit; I Can Trick a Tiger; Super Dad; Floppy and the Bone
Level 4 Developing as a reader	Wet Feet; The Moon Jet; The Red Coat; Quick! Quick!	Missing!; The Raft Race; Dragon Danger; The Spaceship
Level 5 Building confidence in reading	Tiga Fried Rice; Craig Saves the Day; Seasick; Dolphin Rescue	Hungry Floppy; Husky Adventure; Trapped!; Looking after Gran
Level 6 Reading with confidence	Gran's New Blue Shoes; Ice City; Save Pudding Wood; Uncle Max	Hairy-Scary Monster; Mountain Rescue; The Lost Voice; Secret of the Sands

Phonics stories help children practise their sounds and letters, as they learn to do in school.

First stories have been specially written to provide practice in reading everyday language.

OXFORD
UNIVERSITY PRESS

Great Clarendon Street, Oxford OX2 6DP
Text © Roderick Hunt and Annemarie Young 2007
Illustrations © Alex Brychta 2007
First published 2007
This edition published 2012

10 9 8 7 6 5 4 3 2 1
Series Editors: Kate Ruttle, Annemarie Young
British Library Cataloguing in Publication Data available
ISBN: 978-0-19-848793-7
Printed in China by Imago
The characters in this work are the original creation of Roderick Hunt and Alex Brychta who retain copyright in the characters.
With thanks to Dr Veronica Spooner MB BS MRCGP